STEREOPHONICS
YOU GOTTA GO THERE TO COME BACK

GUITAR
TAB
EDITION

Published by:
Universal Music Publishing Group

Exclusive distributors:
Music Sales Limited
Distribution Centre, Newmarket Road,
Bury St Edmunds Suffolk,
IP33 3YB, England.
Music Sales Pty Limited
120 Rothschild Avenue, Rosebery,
NSW 2018, Australia.

Order No. AM977856
ISBN 1-84449-149-8
This book © Copyright 2003 by
Universal Music Publishing Group.

Music arrangements by Arthur Dick.
Music processed by Paul Ewers Music Design.

Printed in the United Kingdom

Your Guarantee of Quality:

As publishers, we strive to produce
every book to the highest commercial
standards.

While endeavouring to retain the
original running order of the recorded
album, the book has been carefully
designed to minimise awkward page
turns and to make playing from it a
real pleasure.

Particular care has been given to
specifying acid-free, neutral-sized paper
made from pulps which have not been
elemental chlorine bleached.

This pulp is from farmed sustainable
forests and was produced with special
regard for the environment.

Throughout, the printing and binding
have been planned to ensure a sturdy,
attractive publication which should give
years of enjoyment.

If your copy fails to meet our high
standards, please inform us and
we will gladly replace it.

www.musicsales.com

**UNIVERSAL MUSIC
PUBLISHING GROUP**

Help Me (She's Out Of Her Mind)

Words & Music by Kelly Jones

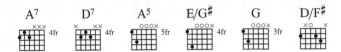

9

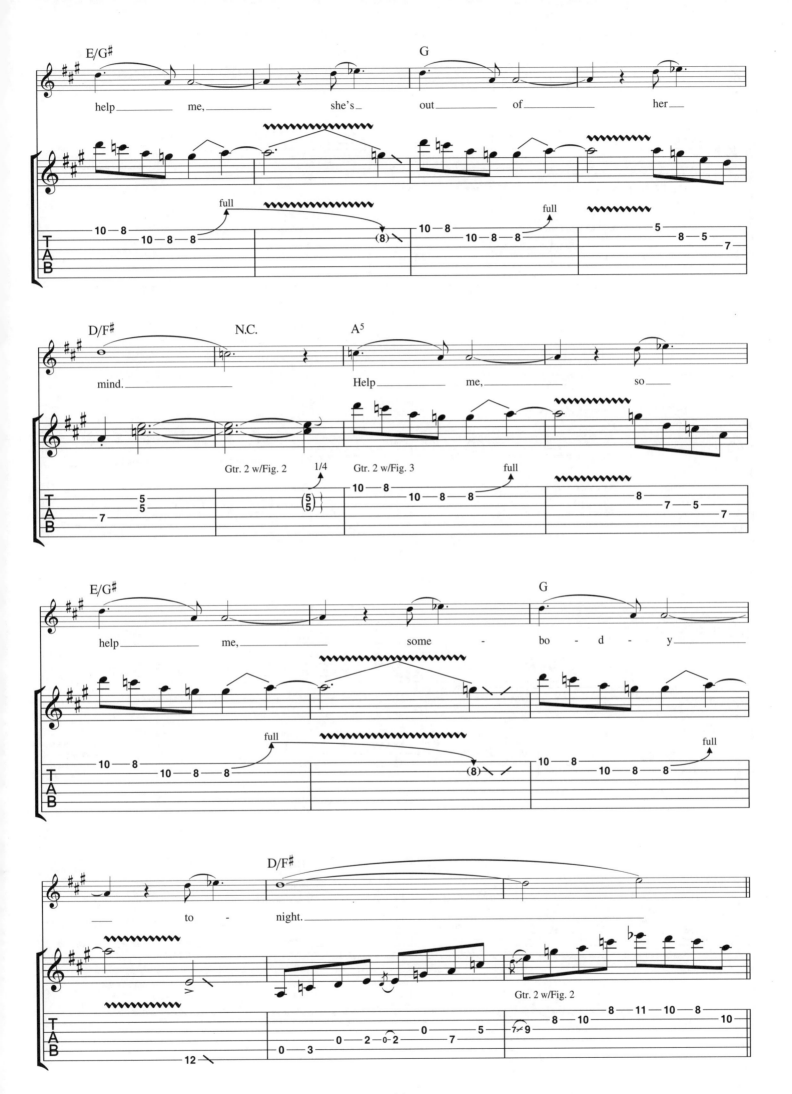

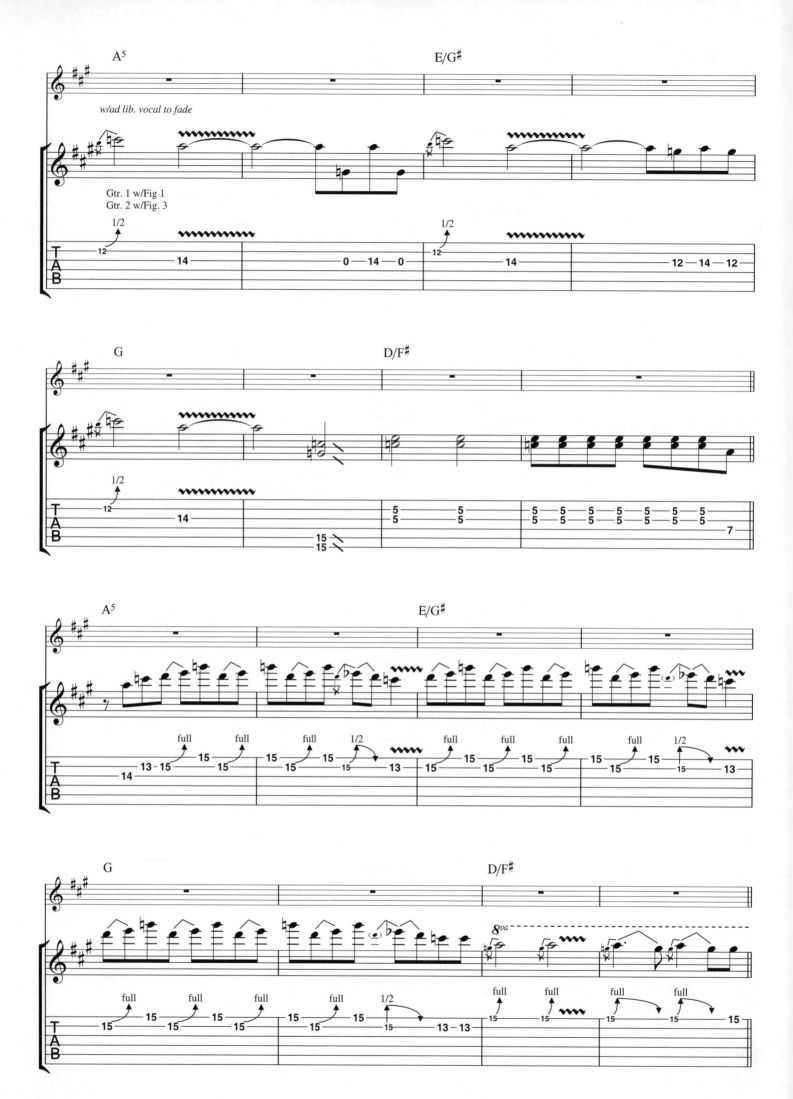

Maybe Tomorrow

Words & Music by Kelly Jones

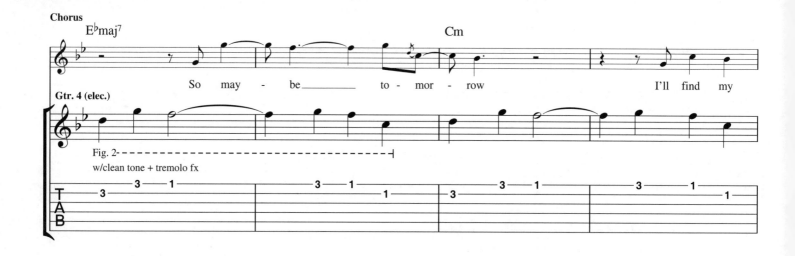

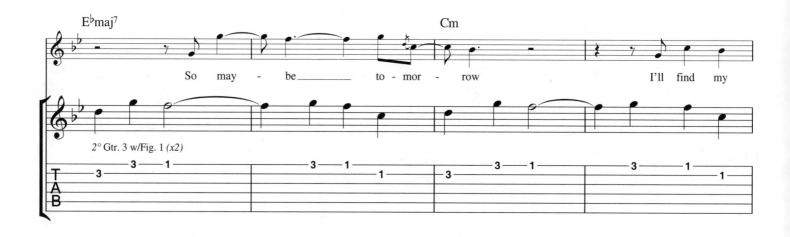

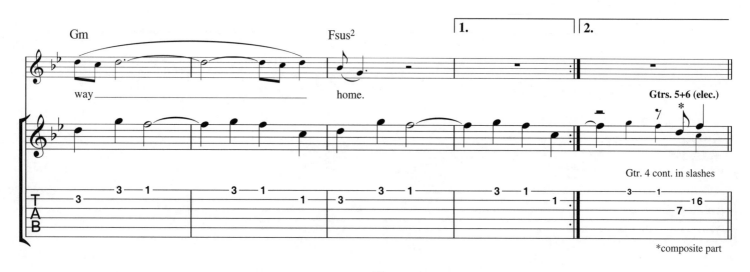

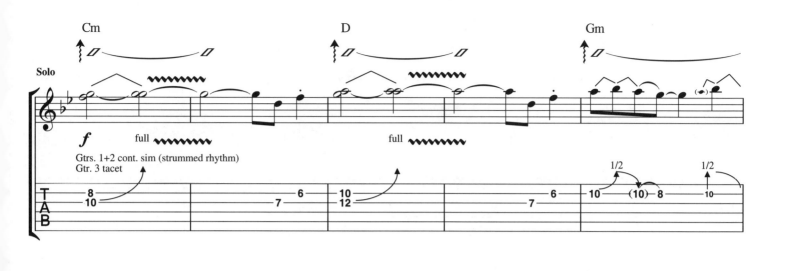

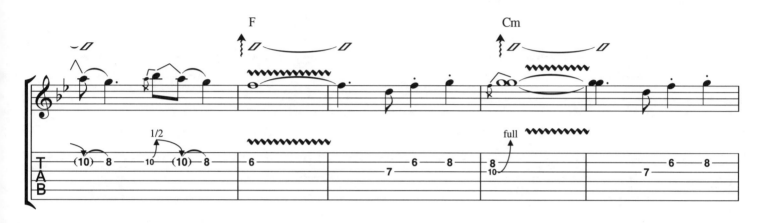

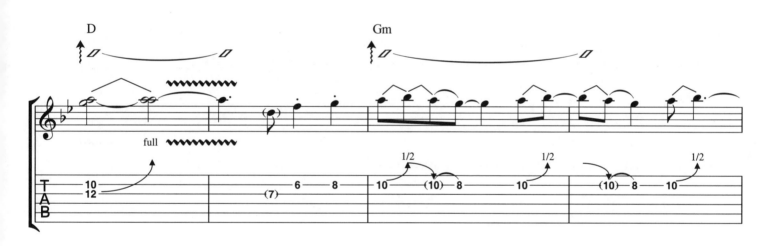

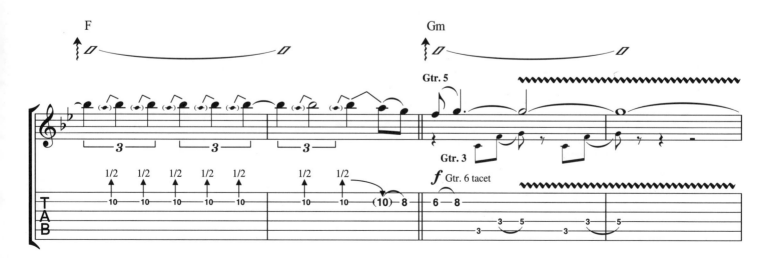

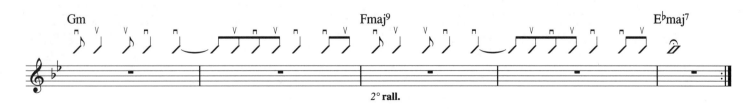

Madame Helga

Words & Music by Kelly Jones

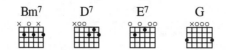

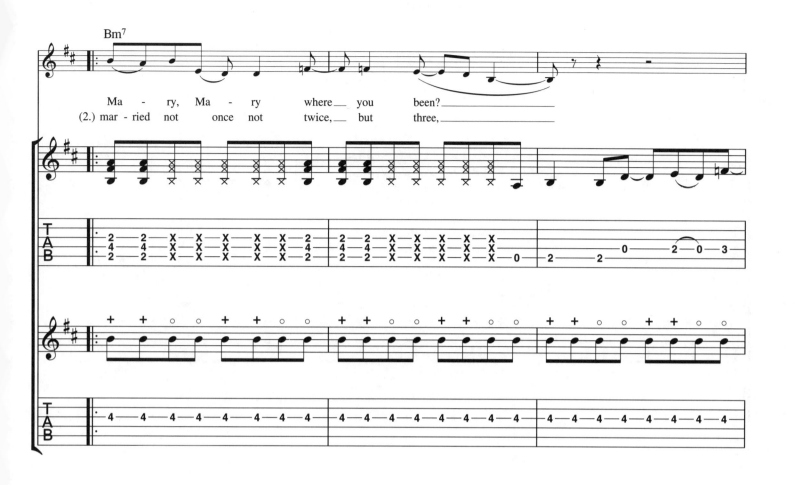

Ma - ry, Ma - ry where you been?
(2.) mar - ried not once not twice, but three,

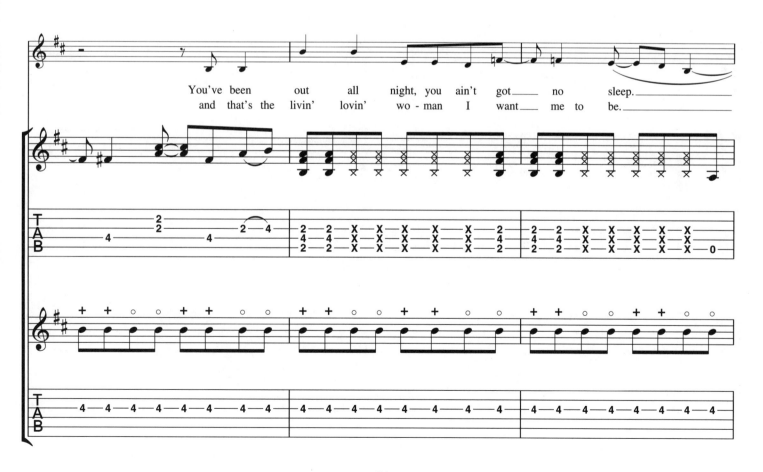

You've been out all night, you ain't got no sleep.
and that's the livin' lovin' wo - man I want me to be.

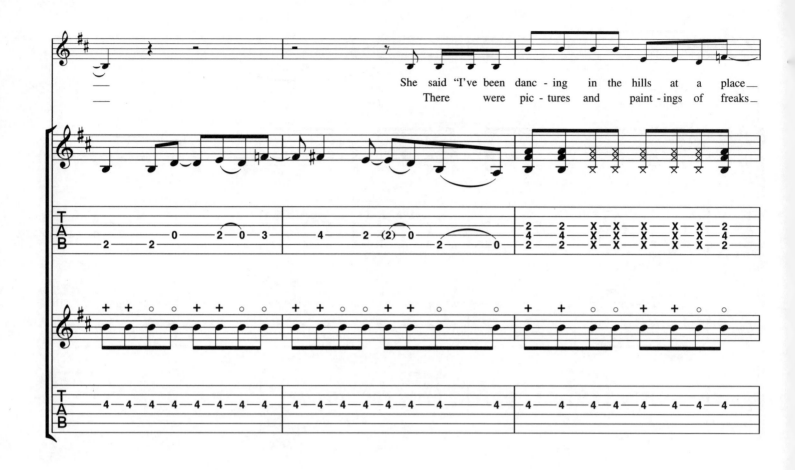

She said "I've been danc - ing in the hills at a place____
There were pic - tures and paint - ings of freaks____

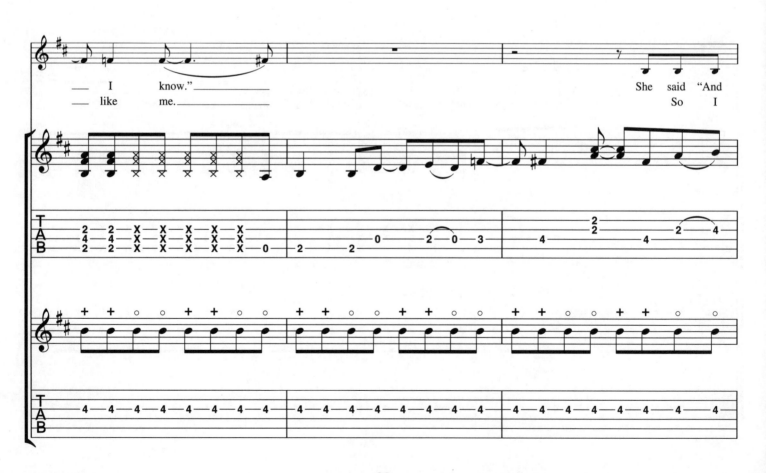

____ I know."____
____ like me.____

She said "And
So I

that   is   the   place   where   the   fire   flies   glow."

drank   with   the   de - vil   for   my   com - pa - ny.

Pre-chorus

D^7

Had   to   slap   my   white   face,   and   pull   my   head   from   the   clouds.

*Gtrs. 1+2

*combined part

23

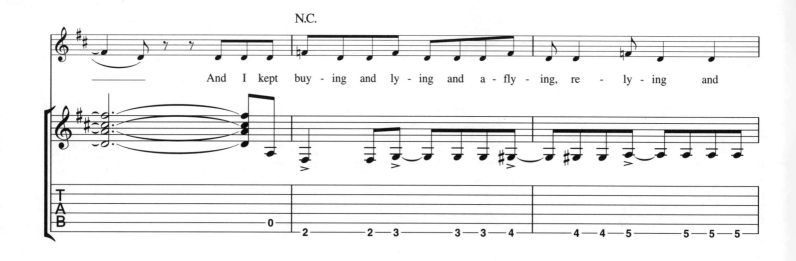

And I kept buy - ing and ly - ing and a - fly - ing, re - ly - ing and

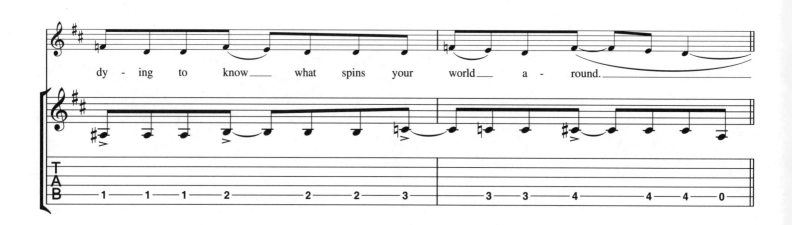

dy - ing to know___ what spins your world___ a - round.___

𝄋 **Chorus**

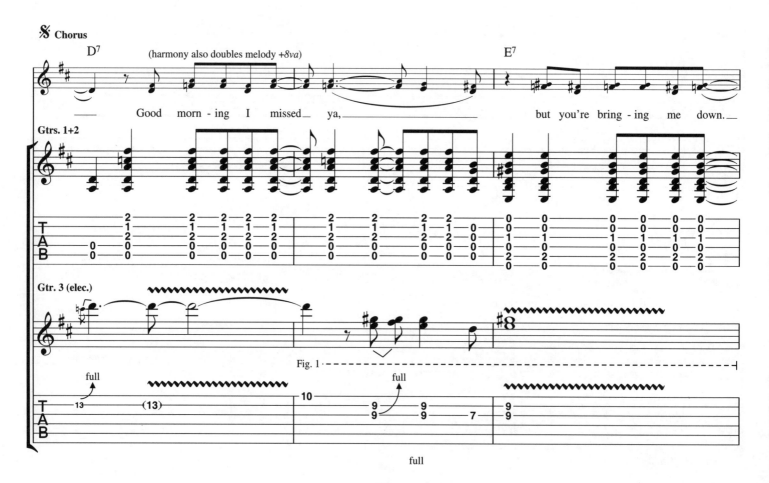

Good morn - ing I missed___ ya,_____ but you're bring - ing me down.___

24

25

You Stole My Money Honey

Words & Music by Kelly Jones

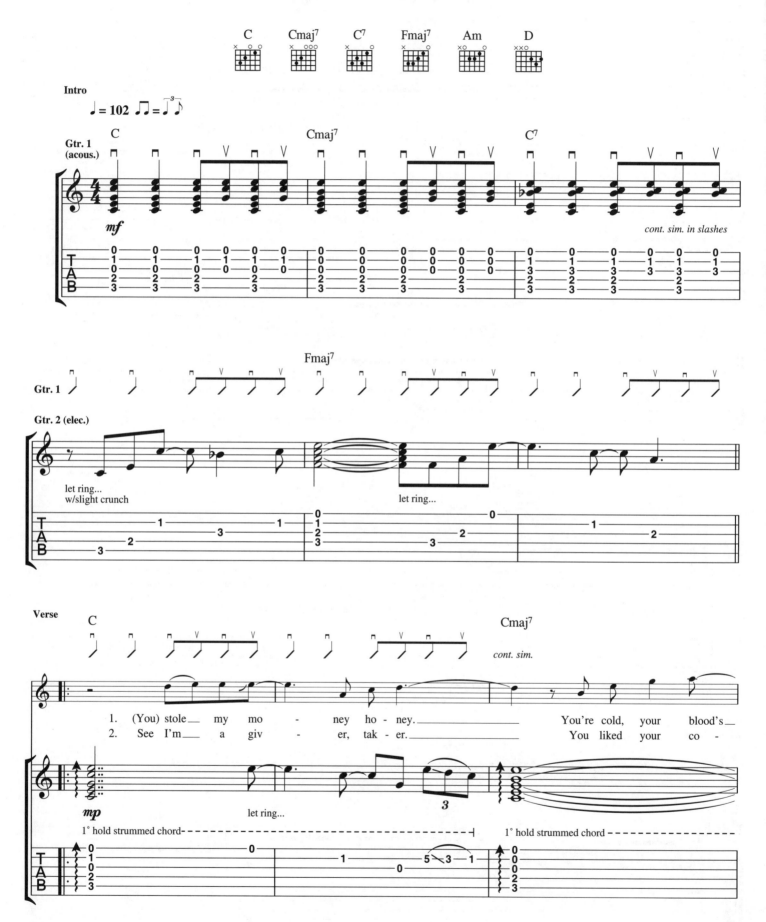

Getaway

Words & Music by Kelly Jones

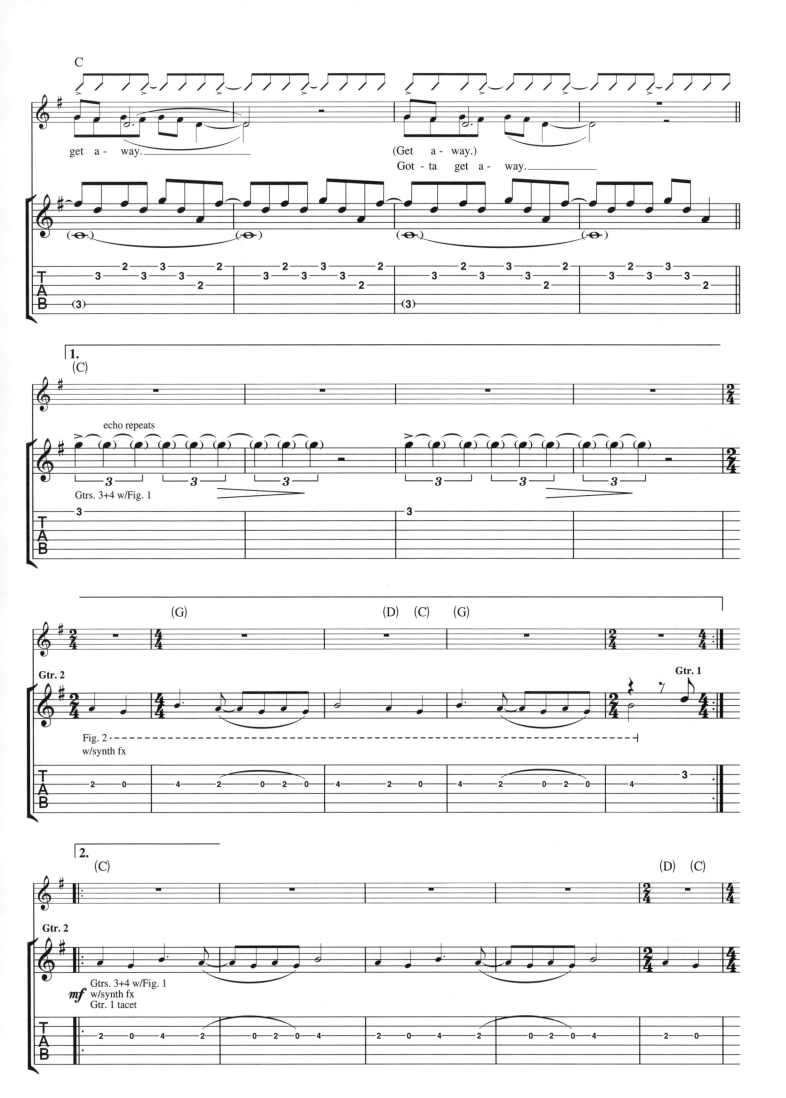

I Miss You Now

Words & Music by Kelly Jones

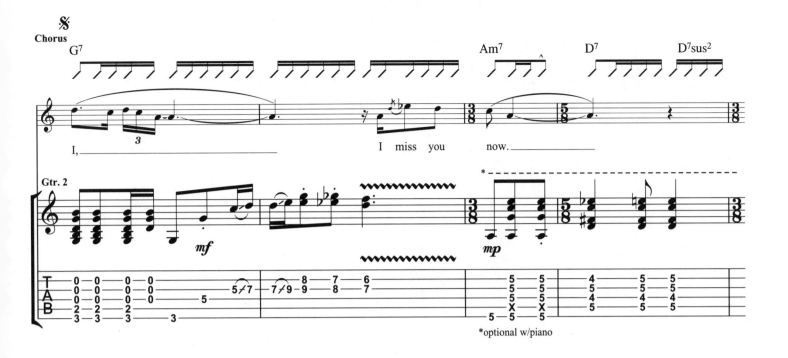

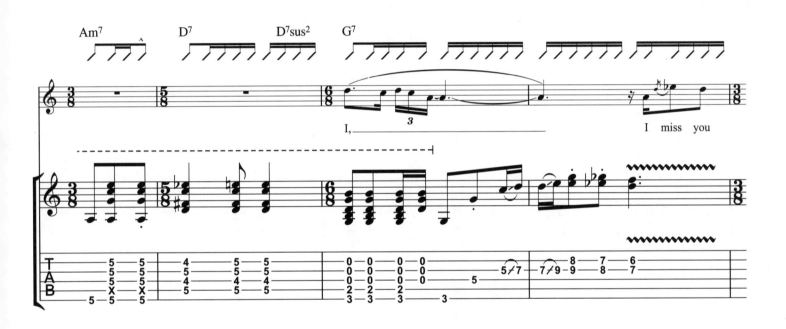

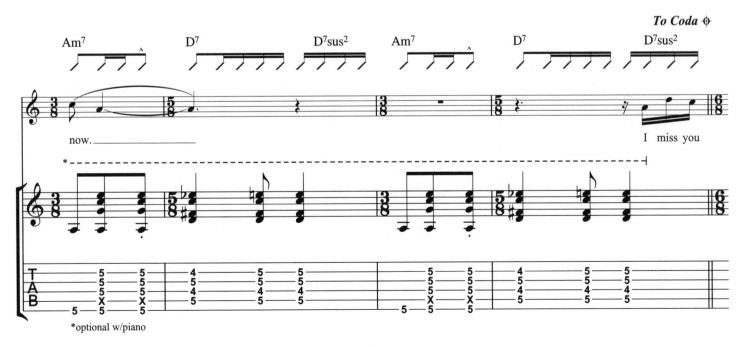

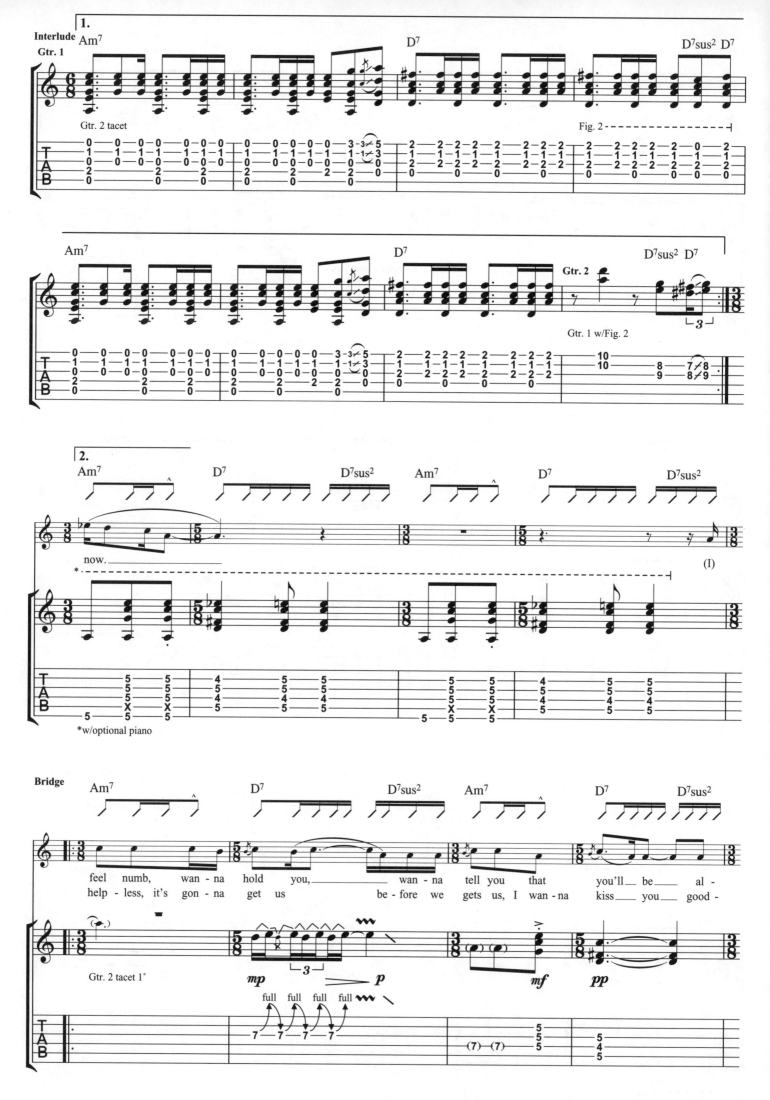

Climbing The Wall

Words & Music by Kelly Jones

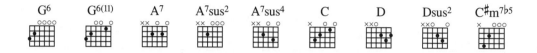

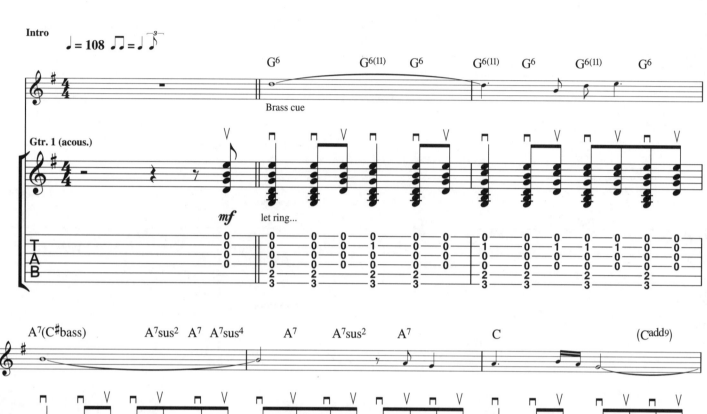

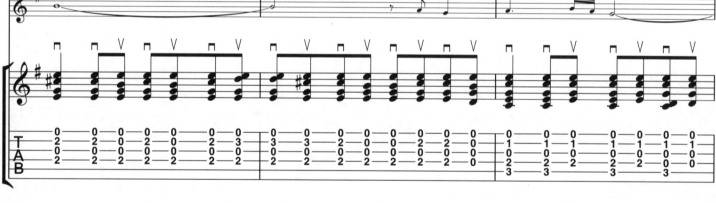

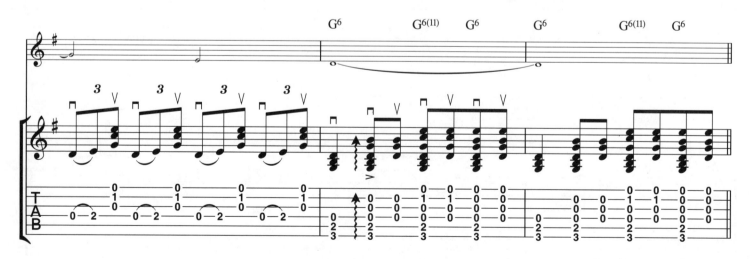

Pre-chorus

Gtr. 3
tacet 1°

let ring...
w/clean tone + chorusing fx

So what makes you___ and what___ makes me?___ What makes {men___ / wo - / peo -

{- men} lie through their teeth?___ {And what makes ten - ton birds fly / And what makes ten - ton ships sail / And what makes ten - ton trains rail}
{- ple}

Gtr. 1 cont. in slashes

46

49

Jealousy

Words & Music by Kelly Jones

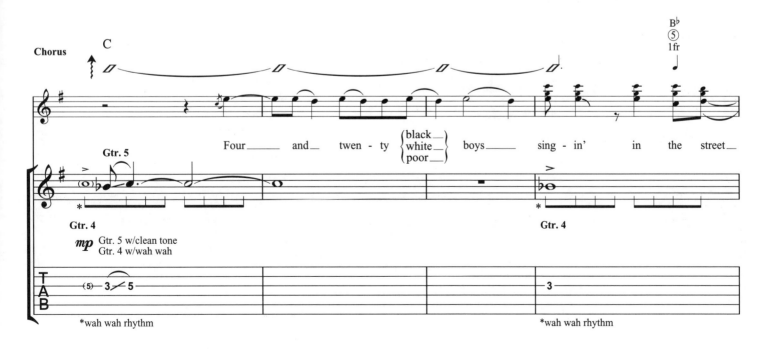

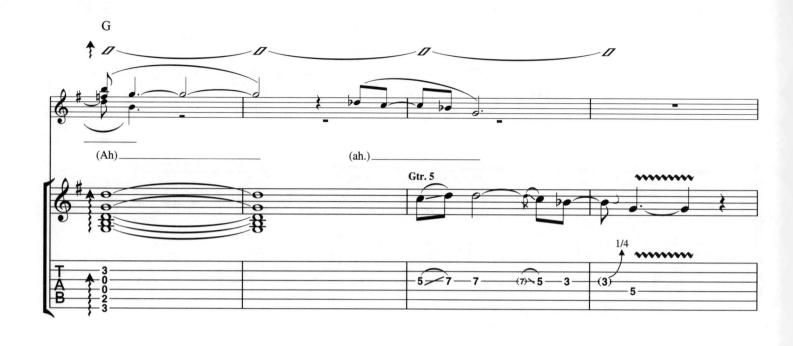

G

(Ah) _____ (ah.) _____

Gtr. 5

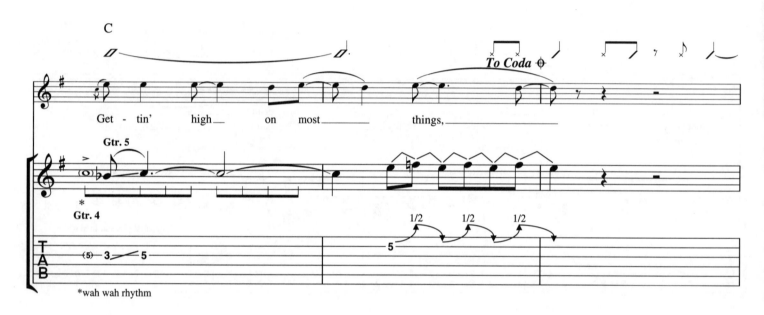

C

Get - tin' high on most things,

Gtr. 5

*
Gtr. 4

*wah wah rhythm

To Coda ⊕

1/2 1/2 1/2

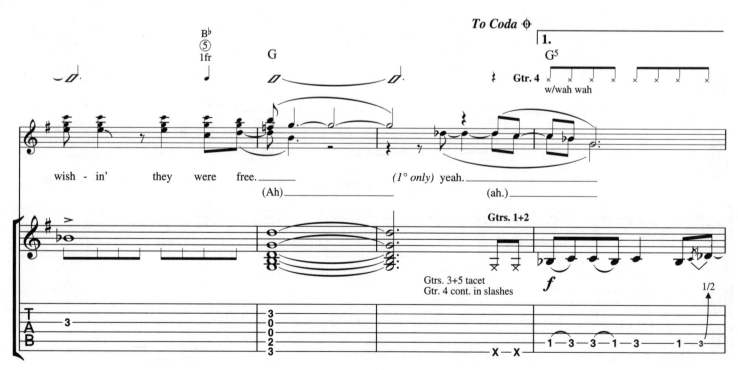

To Coda ⊕

1.

B♭
⑤
1fr

G

G⁵

Gtr. 4
w/wah wah

wish - in' they were free. _____ (1° only) yeah. _____

(Ah) _____ (ah.) _____

Gtrs. 1+2

Gtrs. 3+5 tacet
Gtr. 4 cont. in slashes

f

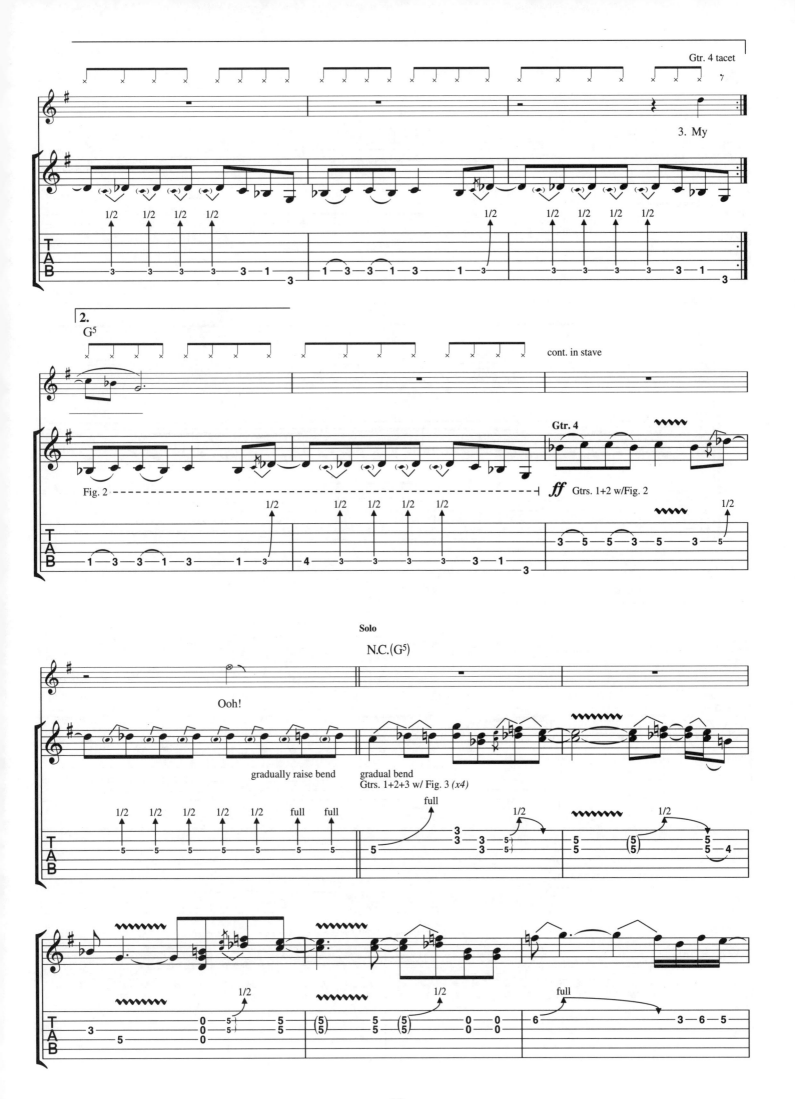

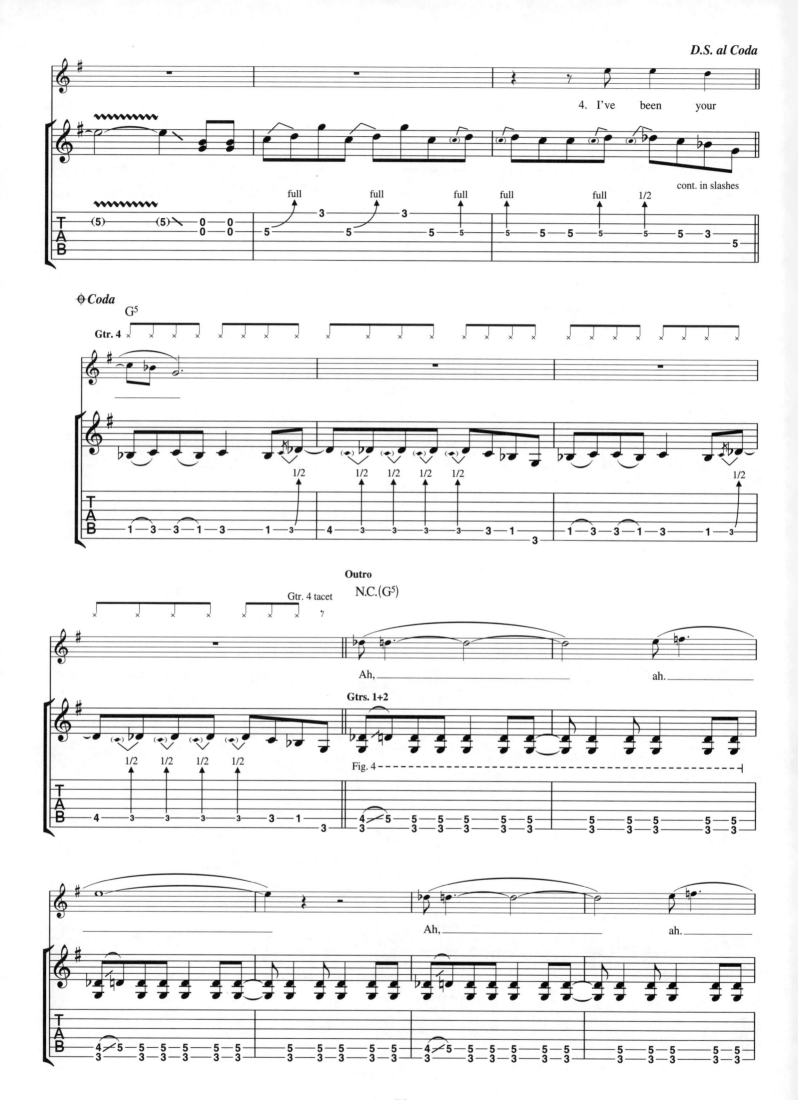

I'm Alright
(You Gotta Go There To Come Back)

Words & Music by Kelly Jones

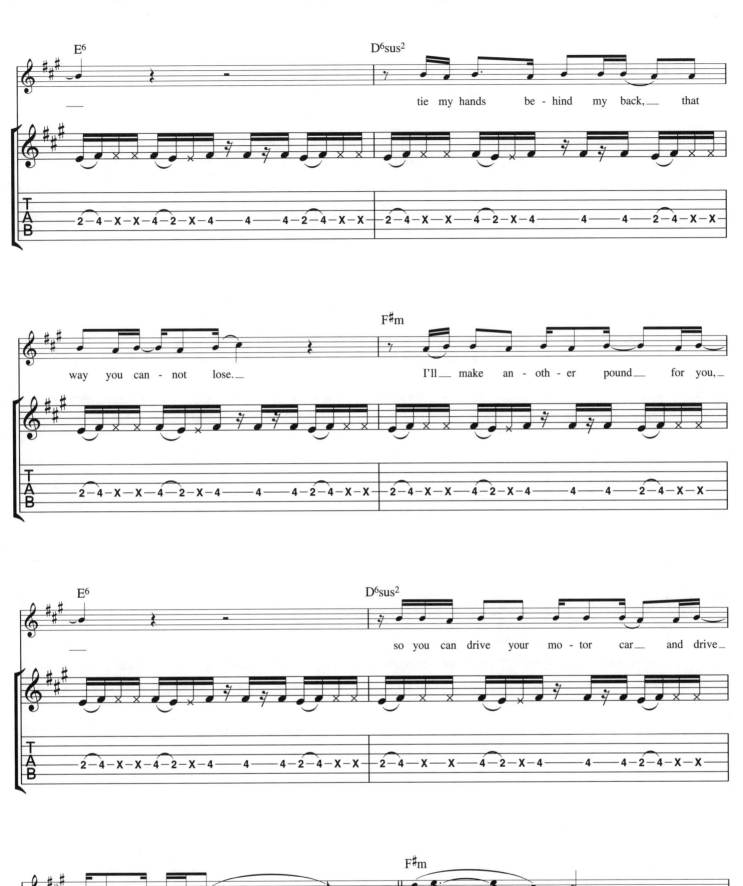

tie my hands be - hind my back, ___ that
way you can - not lose. ___ I'll __ make an - oth - er pound __ for you, __
so you can drive your mo - tor car __ and drive __

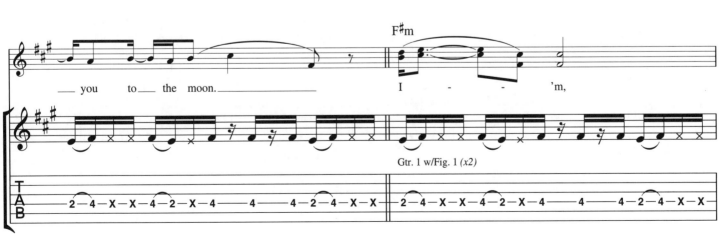

___ you to __ the moon. ___ I - - 'm,

Gtr. 1 w/Fig. 1 *(x2)*

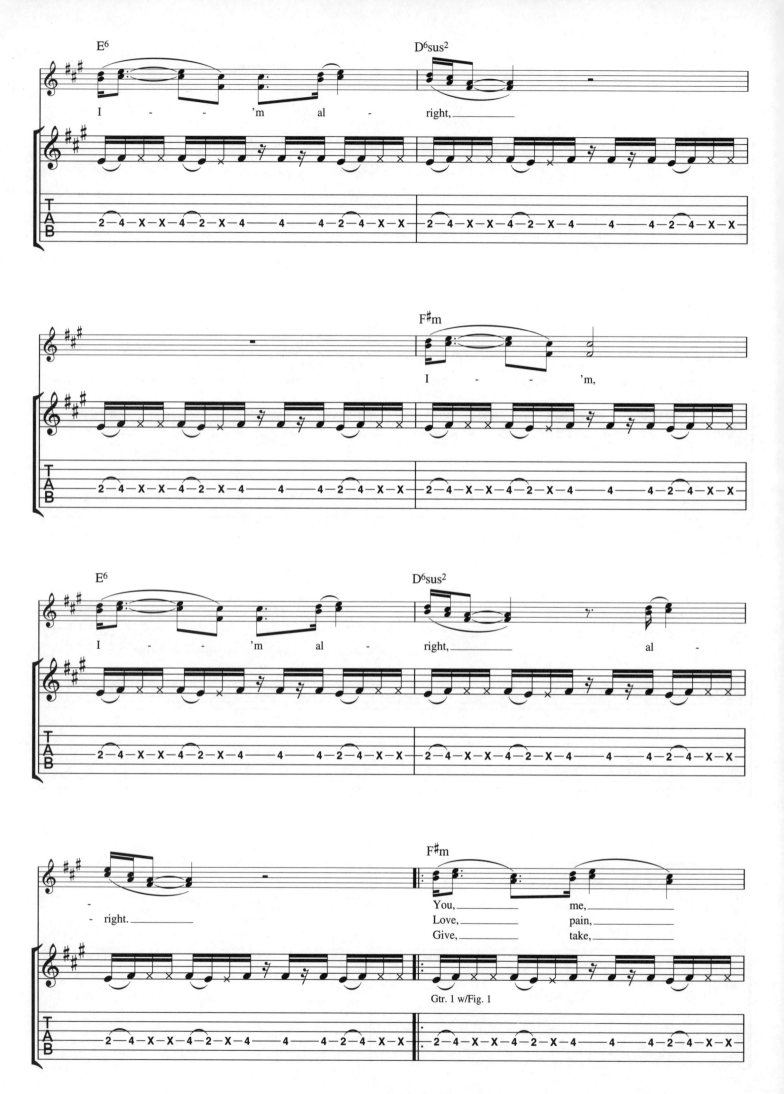

Nothing Precious At All

Words & Music by Kelly Jones

1. I been__ peo - ple watch - in' a - gain,__ I think they watch__ me
2. Gon - na drink her - self__ to sleep__ to - night and that's no - thing

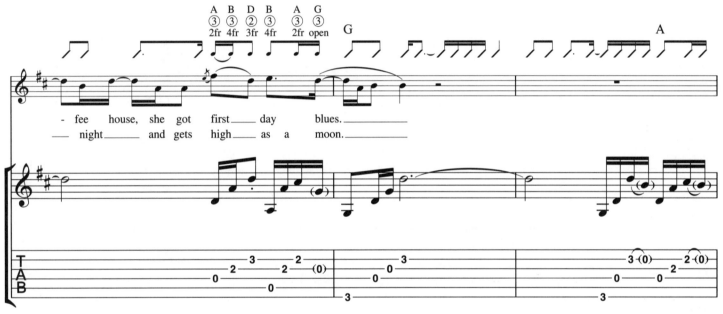

66

look a - round and see what's left___ and it's no - thin' much,___ it's no - thin' pre - cious at all.___

No - thin' pre - cious at all.___

Gtr. 3 tacet

1.   **2.**

Gtr. 3

Fig. 2 -|

Gtr. 3 w/clean tone + slide
Gtr. 1 w/Fig. 2 then
cont. in slashes

Solo

Gtrs. 1+2

Rainbows And Pots Of Gold

Words & Music by Kelly Jones

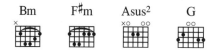

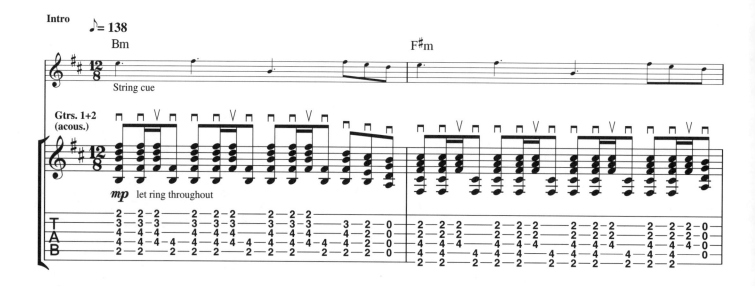

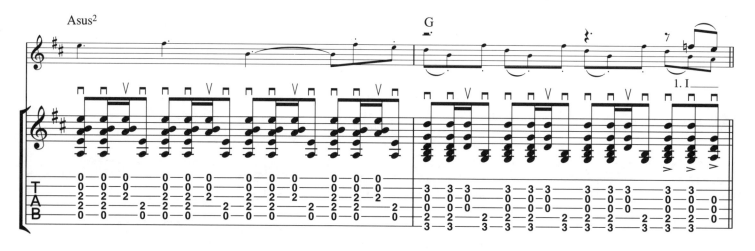

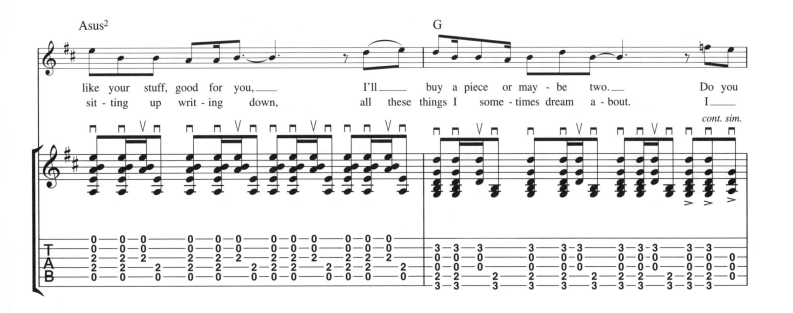

like your stuff, good for you,___ I'll___ buy a piece or may - be two.___ Do you
sit - ting up writ - ing down, all these things I some - times dream a - bout. I___

ev - er think of me?___ D'you re - mem - ber all our___ stu - pid dreams?___
knew your num - ber off by heart, it's the on - ly one I like to talk. It

Rain - bows and pots of gold,___ so much to prove___ be - fore we get old.___ I
was - n't me us - ing you,___ I trust - ed you, one of the few. And we

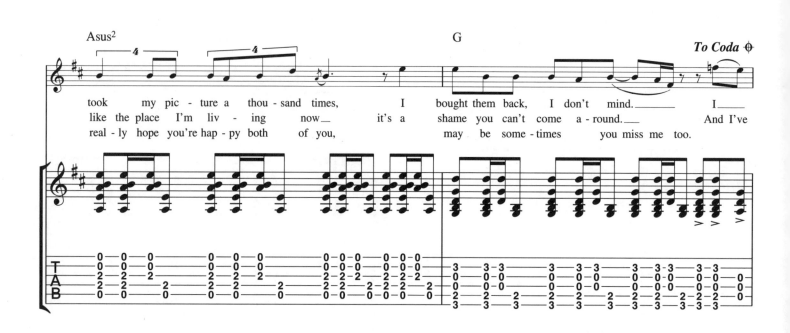

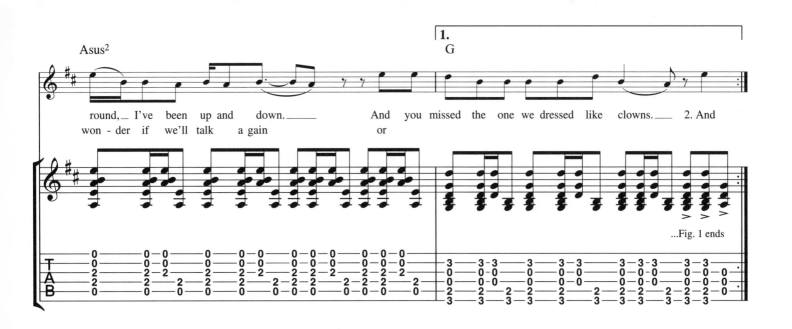

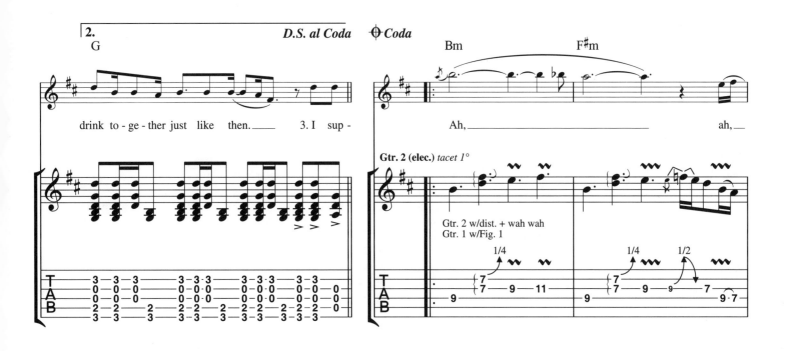

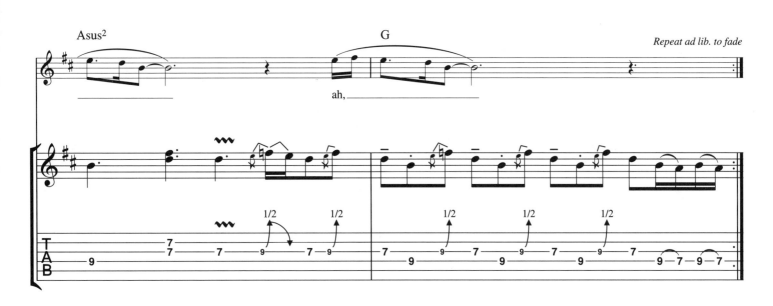

High As The Ceiling

Words & Music by Kelly Jones

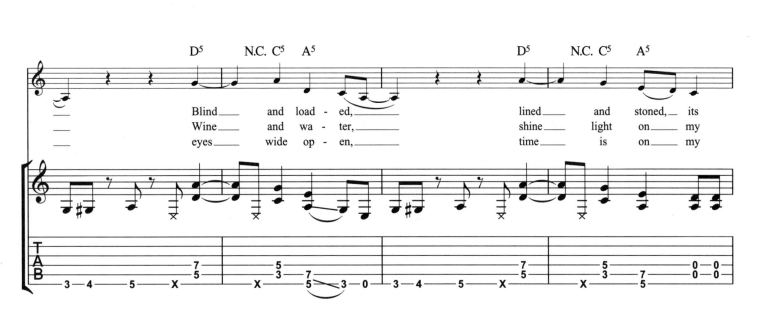

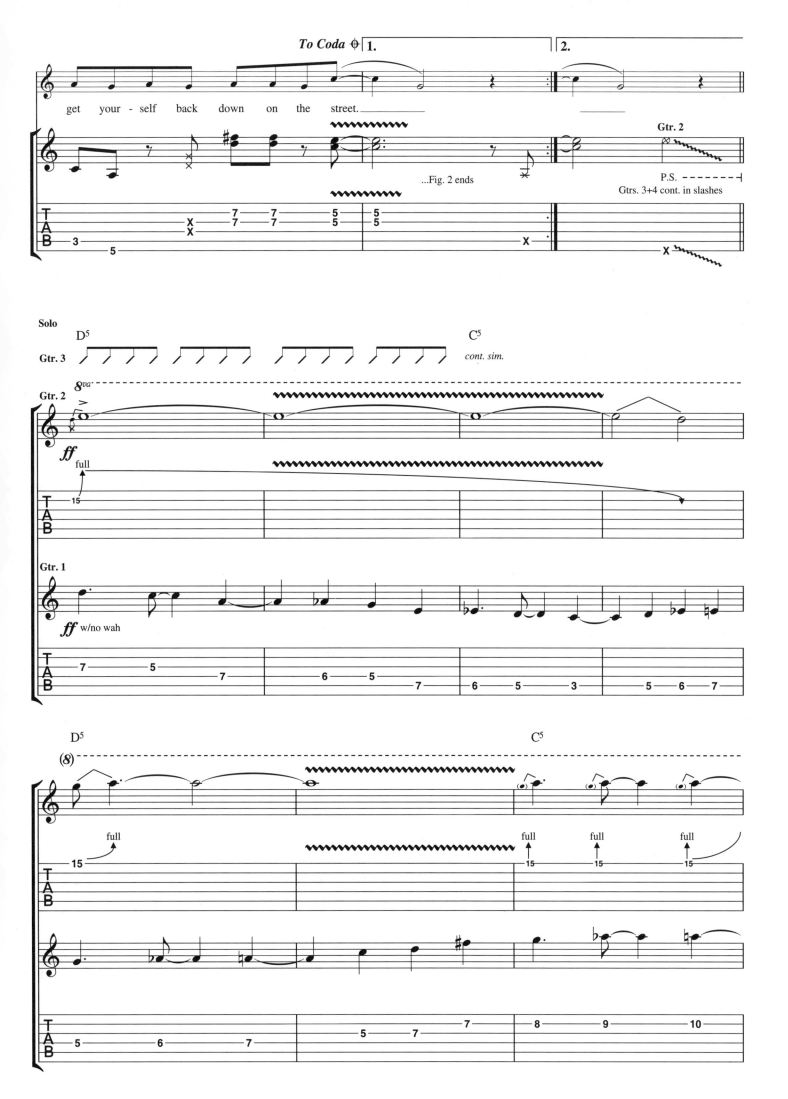

get your-self back down on the street.

*composite part
Gtrs. 1+3+4

78

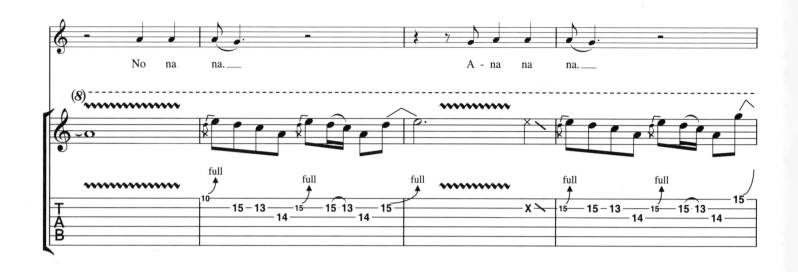

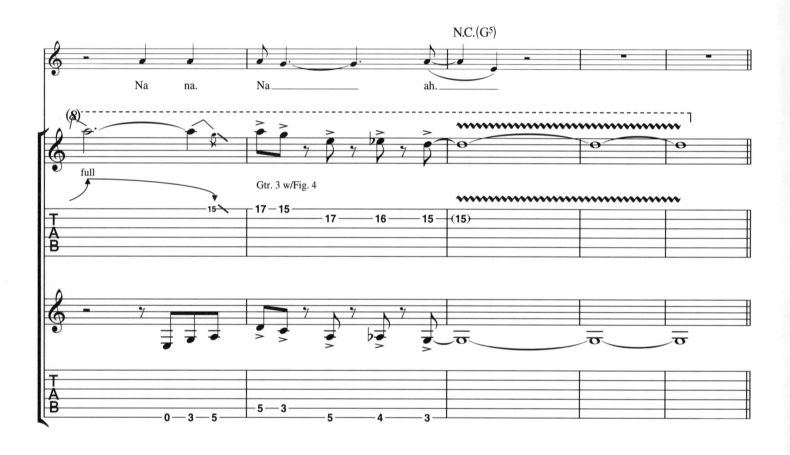

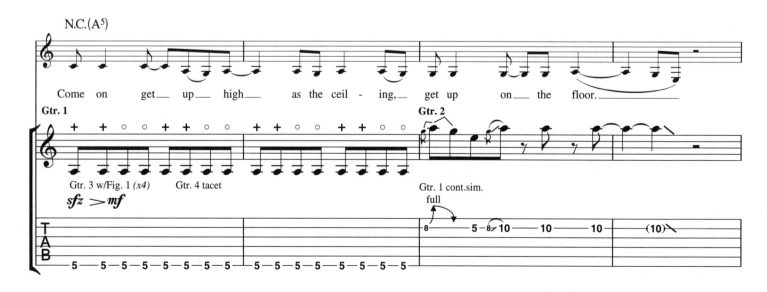

Come on get up high as the ceil-ing, get up on the floor.

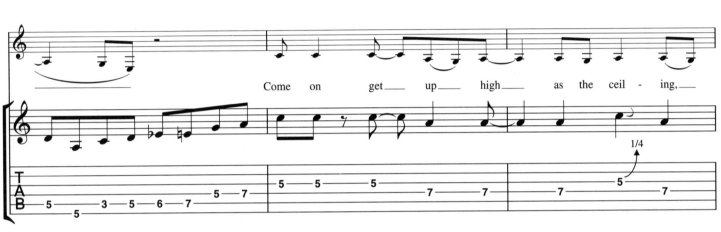

Come on get up high as the ceil - ing,

get up on the floor. I think I lost my mind and I'm feel - ing I've

been there all be - fore. Gtr. 3

Gtrs. 1+2 tacet

Since I Told You It's Over

Words & Music by Kelly Jones

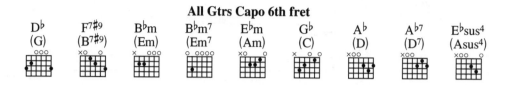

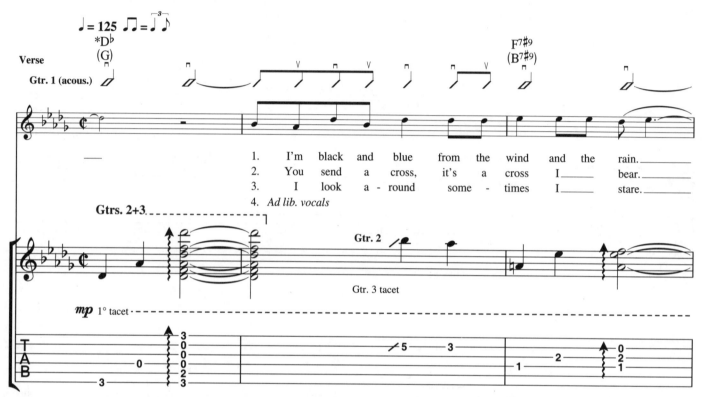

*Symbols in parentheses represent chord names with respect to capoed guitar (TAB 0 = 6th fret).
Symbols above represent actual sounding chords.

Bridge

*composite part,
Gtr. 2 picks ad lib. arpeggios and fills

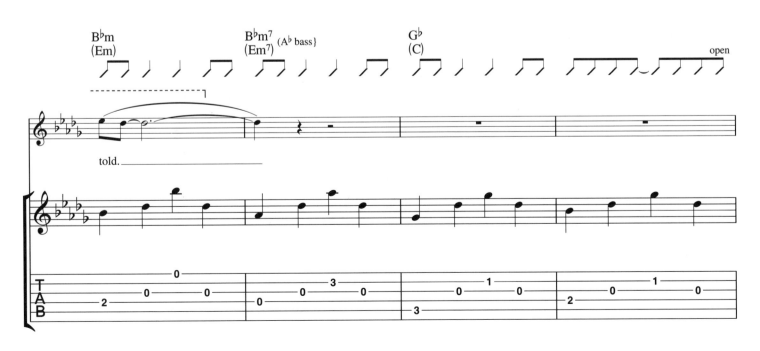

I've been—down, been a-round but I've fall - en on my own—two feet and I've left you out— to drown.—

I nev - er meant for that.—

D.C. with repeats
and fade through Chorus

GUITAR TABLATURE EXPLAINED

Guitar music can be notated three different ways: on a musical stave, in tablature, and in rhythm slashes.

RHYTHM SLASHES are written above the stave. Strum chords in the rhythm indicated. Round noteheads indicate single notes.

THE MUSICAL STAVE shows pitches and rhythms and is divided by lines into bars. Pitches are named after the first seven letters of the alphabet.

TABLATURE graphically represents the guitar fingerboard. Each horizontal line represents a string, and each number represents a fret.

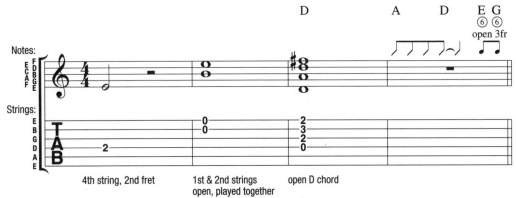

4th string, 2nd fret   1st & 2nd strings open, played together   open D chord

DEFINITIONS FOR SPECIAL GUITAR NOTATION

SEMI-TONE BEND: Strike the note and bend up a semi-tone (1/2 step).

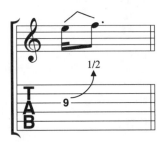

WHOLE-TONE BEND: Strike the note and bend up a whole-tone (whole step).

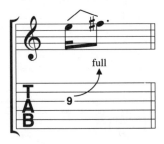

GRACE NOTE BEND: Strike the note and bend as indicated. Play the first note as quickly as possible.

QUARTER-TONE BEND: Strike the note and bend up a 1/4 step.

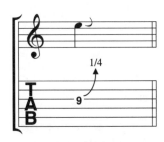

BEND & RELEASE: Strike the note and bend up as indicated, then release back to the original note.

COMPOUND BEND & RELEASE: Strike the note and bend up and down in the rhythm indicated.

PRE-BEND: Bend the note as indicated, then strike it.

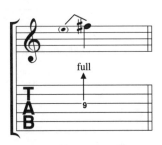

PRE-BEND & RELEASE: Bend the note as indicated. Strike it and release the note back to the original pitch.

UNISON BEND: Strike the two notes simultaneously and bend the lower note up to the pitch of the higher.

BEND & RESTRIKE: Strike the note and bend as indicated then restrike the string where the symbol occurs.

BEND, HOLD AND RELEASE: Same as bend and release but hold the bend for the duration of the tie.

BEND AND TAP: Bend the note as indicated and tap the higher fret while still holding the bend.

VIBRATO: The string is vibrated by rapidly bending and releasing the note with the fretting hand.

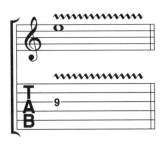

HAMMER-ON: Strike the first note with one finger, then sound the second note (on the same string) with another finger by fretting it without picking.

PULL-OFF: Place both fingers on the notes to be sounded, strike the first note and without picking, pull the finger off to sound the second note.

LEGATO SLIDE (GLISS): Strike the first note and then slide the same fret-hand finger up or down to the second note. The second note is not struck.

87

SHIFT SLIDE (GLISS & RESTRIKE): Same as legato slide, except the second note is struck.

TRILL: Very rapidly alternate between the notes indicated by continuously hammering on and pulling off.

TAPPING: Hammer ("tap") the fret indicated with the pick-hand index or middle finger and pull off to the note fretted by the fret hand.

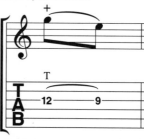

PICK SCRAPE: The edge of the pick is rubbed down (or up) the string, producing a scratchy sound.

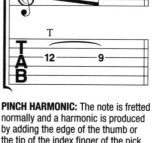

MUFFLED STRINGS: A percussive sound is produced by laying the fret hand across the string(s) without depressing, and striking them with the pick hand.

NATURAL HARMONIC: Strike the note while the fret-hand lightly touches the string directly over the fret indicated.

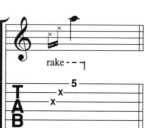

PINCH HARMONIC: The note is fretted normally and a harmonic is produced by adding the edge of the thumb or the tip of the index finger of the pick hand to the normal pick attack.

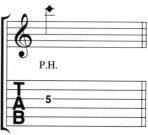

HARP HARMONIC: The note is fretted normally and a harmonic is produced by gently resting the pick hand's index finger directly above the indicated fret (in brackets) while plucking the appropriate string.

PALM MUTING: The note is partially muted by the pick hand lightly touching the string(s) just before the bridge.

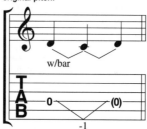

RAKE: Drag the pick across the strings indicated with a single motion.

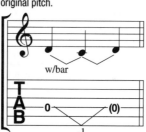

TREMOLO PICKING: The note is picked as rapidly and continuously as possible.

ARPEGGIATE: Play the notes of the chord indicated by quickly rolling them from bottom to top.

SWEEP PICKING: Rhythmic downstroke and/or upstroke motion across the strings.

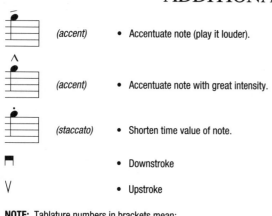

VIBRATO DIVE BAR AND RETURN: The pitch of the note or chord is dropped a specific number of steps (in rhythm) then returned to the original pitch.

VIBRATO BAR SCOOP: Depress the bar just before striking the note, then quickly release the bar.

VIBRATO BAR DIP: Strike the note and then immediately drop a specific number of steps, then release back to the original pitch.

ADDITIONAL MUSICAL DEFINITIONS

(accent)	•	Accentuate note (play it louder).
(accent)	•	Accentuate note with great intensity.
(staccato)	•	Shorten time value of note.
■	•	Downstroke
V	•	Upstroke

D.%. al Coda

• Go back to the sign (%), then play until the bar marked *To Coda* ⊕ then skip to the section marked ⊕ *Coda*.

D.C. al Fine

• Go back to the beginning of the song and play until the bar marked *Fine*.

tacet

• Instrument is silent (drops out).

• Repeat bars between signs.

|1. |2.

• When a repeated section has different endings, play the first ending only the first time and the second ending only the second time.

NOTE: Tablature numbers in brackets mean:
1. The note is sustained, but a new articulation (such as hammer on or slide) begins.
2. A note may be fretted but not necessarily played.